# The PYRAMID of DOOM

written and illustrated
by
NICK ABADZIS

For Natalie

# Chapter One

It is a still night, somewhere in Africa.

This is Zakuma, a small town near the edge of a great desert.

Tom Baxter is here on holiday with his father.

As Tom sleeps, his father waits for a visitor.

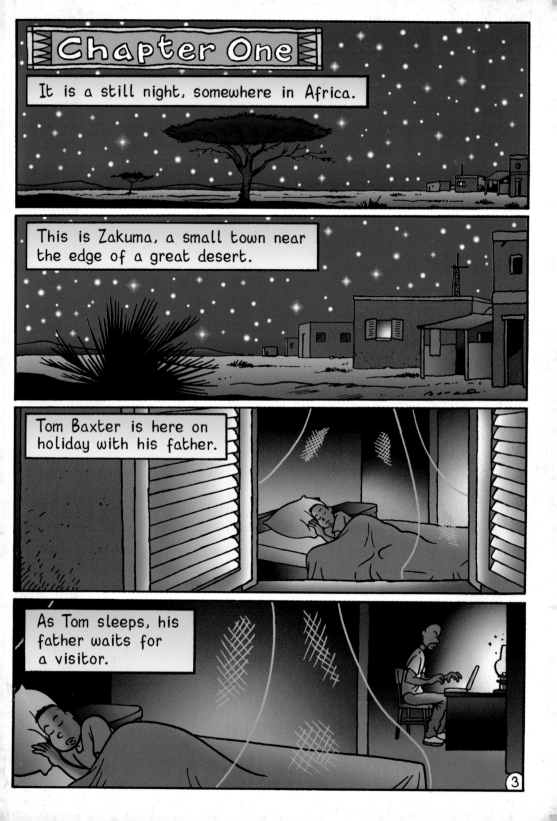

Tom's father is the famous archaeologist, Dr William Baxter.

KNOCK! KNOCK!

At last!

Mohammed, welcome.

I have something for you, Dr Baxter.

I am giving it to you because you are my friend and I can trust you.

Through the ages, many have tried to find the dark pyramid.

A map!

They have either vanished, or returned mad.

I know you are curious, but the pyramid is hidden for a reason. You will be the first archaeologist to see it.

Take my advice. *Look, but do not enter.*

I'll do as you say. And I'll make sure the pyramid stays hidden.

I trust you. Take care, Dr Baxter.

Thank you, Mohammed.

Dawn.

5

Dr Baxter loads up his jeep. He doesn't know he's being watched.

It's Professor Henry Mace, another archaeologist, with his daughter, Jodie.

I knew it was a good idea to follow Baxter to Africa. He's not just on holiday. He's *found* something!

Yeah, Dad. We're supposed to be on holiday, too. Remember?

Sssh!

We drove all night to get here. Can't we sleep now?

Soon.

First I need to put this *tracking device* on Baxter's jeep so we don't lose him.

!

Done!

CLICK!

Now I can link my laptop computer in to the *global satellite tracking network*. I can find Baxter anywhere!

BLEEP!

Z

Nearby...

?

Tom! Wake up, son.

7

8

Days of travelling pass.

Tom and his father follow the map over some rough country. It takes them deep into a chain of low mountains.

It's a lonely place where very few people have ever been.

Mace follows at a distance.

On the fourth day, there is a sandstorm.

Dad, this map's not very good.

It's very *old*, Tom.

9

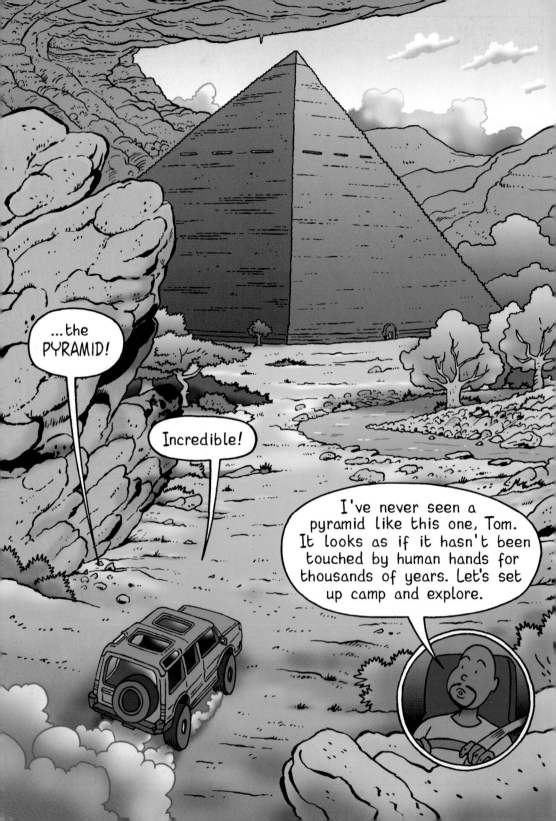

13

Ancient hogwash!

Mace – just calm down!

Let's sleep on it before we decide what to do.

Agreed. It's late. We can talk in the morning.

Mace always follows you. He's jealous of the respect you get.

How did he find me *here*?

I must think of a way of stopping him from telling the world.

16

Jodie's in my class at school, you know. We're not mates – she's always grumpy.

If I had **her** dad, I'd be grumpy, too.

Ha, ha! Let's get some sleep.

The next morning...

Dr Baxter!

Dr Baxter, wake up! My dad's gone missing!

Jodie?

?

Two minutes later...

!

Dad, look!

Oh, no! He's broken into the pyramid!

17

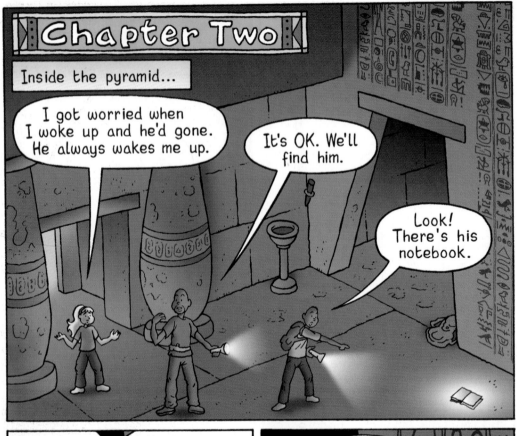

Chapter Two

Inside the pyramid...

I got worried when I woke up and he'd gone. He always wakes me up.

It's OK. We'll find him.

Look! There's his notebook.

Strange. Why would he leave that here?

He must have been decoding the hieroglyphics on this wall.

Hmmm.

Two small cubes are the key to this pyramid

dark    Light

"Do not separate the magic cubes. *This will set the great snake free.*"

AARGH!

Jodie!

Quickly, Tom ties the end of a ball of string, from his backpack, to a pillar.

This way we can find our way back to the entrance.

WHOA!

Dad!

21

23

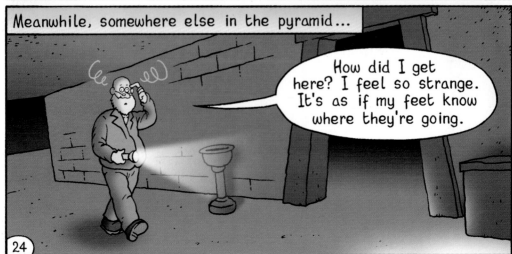

25

27

Meanwhile, Mace is being guided by the voice of the great snake.

28

NOW YOU ARE COMPLETELY IN MY POWER!

I serve only you, o great snake!

Now bring it to the gateway. All you need to do to help me through is read the magic words on the *dark* cube.

I obey!

We must follow him.

How? There are mummies all around us!

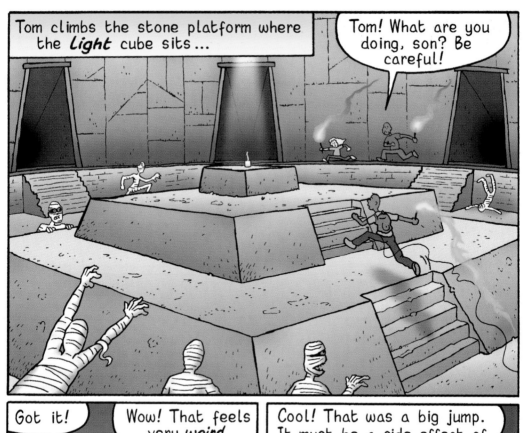

Chapter Three

Tom climbs the stone platform where the *Light* cube sits...

Tom! What are you doing, son? Be careful!

Got it!

Wow! That feels very **weird**.

Cool! That was a big jump. It must be a side effect of the magic.

?

As the great snake crosses from its world into ours, it hisses a cry of freedom.
SSSSSS!
Master!

40

Instead, she hurls her burning torch at the snake.

**All** snakes are afraid of fire!

EEEEE

Then she grabs the **dark** cube from her father with her bandaged hand.

NO!

And **then** she runs.

They all run. They run like they have never run in their lives.

There is a rumbling sound. Everything starts to shake.

The pyramid starts to crumble. Something is coming.

Something *huge.*

CRACK!

CRACK!

CRAAACK!

ROOOAAAR!

Something that is very, very *angry.*

42

THE GREAT SNAKE COMES!

CRUNNNCH!

TOM!

CLACK!

NOOoo!

We've done it!

Yeah. Wow!

But then the snake spits its venom at the cubes!

Oh, no!

SPLAAAT!

43

**EEEEeeeee!**

**SLUUURRP!**

When the dust clears...

The whole pyramid got sucked through the gateway. An incredible discovery, gone for ever.

Who cares, Dad? The snake's gone!

Look. It meant to destroy the *light* cube with its venom, but it actually melted them together. They don't seem very magic anymore.

Good. Now it's locked in its own world for ever.

Jodie?

My dad was in there!

Dr Baxter saved my life *twice* today. Shouldn't you be thanking him?

And Jodie saved ours. You should be proud, Mace. You have a very brave daughter.

I'm – I'm sorry.

Baxter, can we just pretend all this never happened?

I'll keep quiet, if you do, Mace. We'll both look silly talking about a pyramid that's vanished.

Soon...

Don't worry, Dr Baxter. I'll keep an eye on him.

The End